RKLING ARRANGEMENTS FOR MIXED VOICE CHOIRS
AND INTRODUCED BY RALPH ALLWOOD

NOVELLO

Published in Great Britain by

Novello Publishing Limited
Head Office:
Novello & Company Limited
14-15 Berners Street, London W1T 3LJ
Telephone: +44 (0)20 7612 7400
Fax: +44 (0)20 7612 7545

Sales & Hire:
Music Sales Limited
Newmarket Road, Bury St Edmunds,
Suffolk IP33 3YB England
Telephone: +44 (0)1284 702 600
Fax: +44 (0)1284 768 301

Cover illustration and design by Liz Barrand.
Back cover photograph:
Ralph Allwood by Tom Allwood. www.tomallwood.com

NOV957220
ISBN 978-1-84938-293-9

e-mail: music@musicsales.co.uk
www.chesternovello.com

Printed in Great Britain

Other anthologies by Ralph Allwood available from Novello:

By Popular Request NOV072524
By Special Arrangement NOV072523
German Romantic Motets: Brahms to Mendelssohn NOV078639
German Romantic Motets: Reger to Wolf NOV078640
Pearsall Partsongs (Book 1) NOV451638
Pearsall Partsongs (Book 2) NOV451649
Russian Choral Masterpieces NOV310801

Christmas Pops! will be on every choral singer and director's Christmas list. Here is the perfect resource of popular Christmas classics skilfully and wittily arranged for SATB chorus, which will add sparkle - even glitz - to every Christmas choral concert, causing audience and singers to stamp, drool and demand more.

We have filled this collection with twelve accessible and inventive arrangements by the cream (mostly) of today's choral arrangers. Popular hits of recent years sit enticingly wrapped alongside traditional classics such as *Jingle Bells* which will be appreciated by audiences and singers of all tastes. Accompanists will revel in John Gardner's classic *We wish you a merry Christmas* and Matthew O'Donovan's inventive, jazzy *See amid the winter's snow*, while the young at heart (that is, all who choose to sing) will delight in performing Hywel Davies's ridiculous *I want a hippopotamus for Christmas* and Jonathan Wikeley's *When Santa got stuck up the chimney*.

Each arrangement is carefully presented with suggested directions to coach effective performances. Non-threatening rehearsal accompaniments are provided for each a cappella arrangement.

There is an exciting wealth of new material here to suit you.

Merry Christmas!

Ralph Allwood
Eton College, 2009

ALL I WANT FOR CHRISTMAS IS YOU

Words and music by
MARIAH CAREY and WALTER AFANASIEFF

arranged by
MATTHEW O'DONOVAN

5
Bass solo
I just want you for my own, more than you could ev - er know.
cresc.
oh
oh
oh
oh
7
f
lunga
G.P.
Make my wish come true, all I want for Christ-mas is
tutti

10
Allegro (♩. = 150) with a festive bounce
da ba da ba da ba da ba da ba da ba da ba da ba da ba da ba da ba da ba
da ba da ba da ba da ba da ba da ba da ba da ba da ba da ba da ba da ba
da ba da ba da ba da ba da ba da ba da ba da ba
da ba da ba da ba da ba
Allegro (♩. = 150) with a festive bounce
13
ff
mf
da ba da ba
da ba da ba da ba da ba da ba da ba da ba da ba
f marcato
I don't want a lot for Christ - mas,
da ba da ba
f marcato
I don't want a lot for Christ - mas,
da ba da ba doo doo doo doo doo doo doo doo doo

16
f marcato
da ba da ba da ba da ba da ba da ba da ba da ba I don't care a - bout
mf
there is just one_ thing I need, da ba da ba da ba da ba
più f
there is just one_ thing I need, and I_
doo doo doo doo doo doo doo doo doo doo doo doo

19
_ the_ pre - sents_ un - der - neath_ the Christ - mas tree._
più f
da ba da ba da and I_
doo doo doo doo de li doo doo doo doo doo doo doo doo

mf
la la la la la la la la la la la la la la la la la la la la la la la la
mf
la la la la la la la la la la la la la la la la la la la la la la la la
I don't need to hang my stock - ing there up - on the fire -
f
ah
f
And I
f
la la la la la and I
f marcato
la la la la la la la San - ta Claus won't make me hap - py
- place.
meno f
ah
doo doo doo doo doo doo doo doo doo doo doo ba

28
mf cresc.
I just want you for my own
mf cresc.
oo
mf cresc.
with a toy on Christ - mas day.
oo
ah
mf cresc.
doo doo doo doo doo doo doo doo
I just want you for my own

32
f
more than you could ev - er know.
Make my wish come true
f
oo
Make my wish come true ba - by
f
oo
Make my wish come true ba - by
f
more than you could ev - er know.
Make my wish come true ba - by

36
all I want for Christ-mas is you,
all I want for Christ-mas is you,
all I want for Christ-mas is you, ba da ba da ba da ba da ba da ba da ba da ba
all I want for Christ-mas is you, doo doo doo doo doo doo doo

40
mp
you, ba - by. Oh, I won't ask for much
p
you, ba - by. da ba da ba da ba da ba
p
da ba da ba da ba da ba da ba da ba da ba da ba da ba da ba da ba da ba
p
doo doo doo doo doo ba da ba da doo oo

43
this Christ - mas,
I won't e - ven
wish for snow.
mp
da ba da ba da ba da ba da ba da ba da ba da ba da ba da ba da and I.
mp
da ba da ba da ba da ba da ba da ba da ba da ba da ba da ba da and I.
mp
and I.

46
I'm just gon - na keep on wait - ing un - der - neath the
ba da ba
ba da ba
ba da ba

mis - tle - toe.
la la la la la la la la la la la la la la la la
la la la la la la la la la la la la la la la la la la la la la la la
I won't make a list and send it
to the North Pole for Saint Nick.
I won't e - ven stay a - wake to
doo wah
gliss.

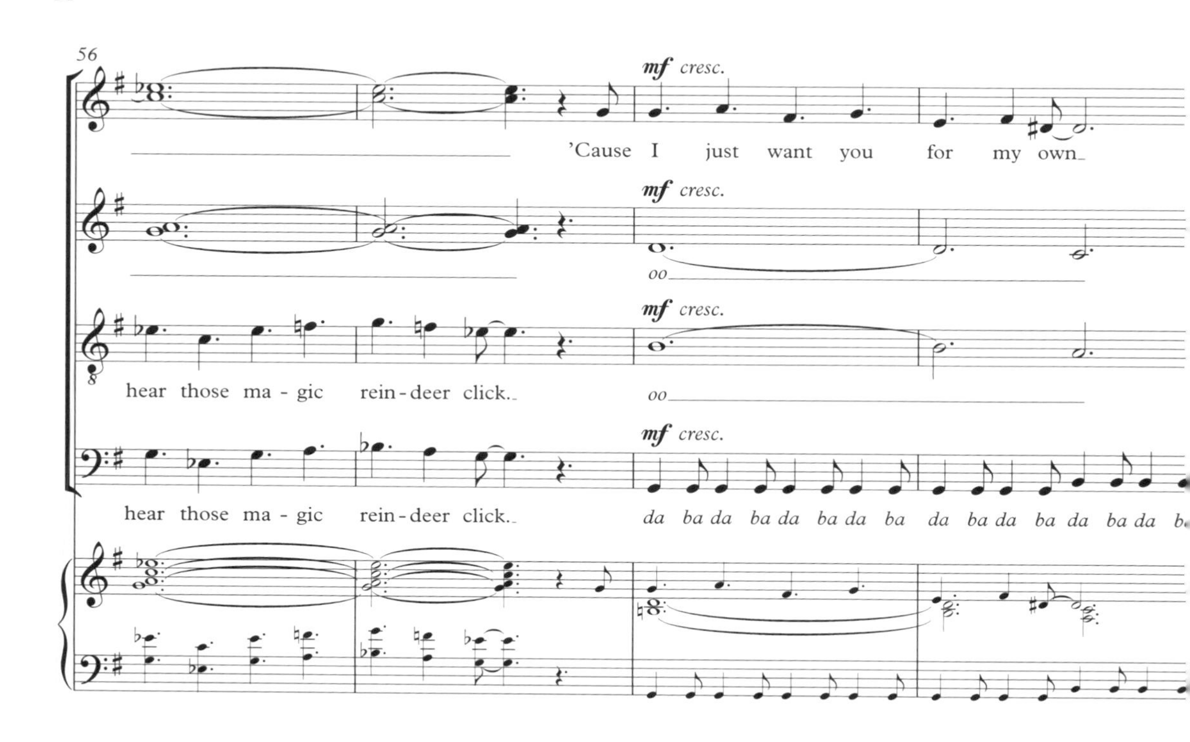
56
mf cresc.
'Cause I just want you for my own
oo
hear those ma - gic rein - deer click.
da ba da ba da ba da ba da ba da ba da ba da b

60
f
more than you could ev - er know.
Make my wish come true ba - b
oo
da ba da ba da ba da ba da ba da ba da ba da

64
all I want for Christ-mas is you,
all I want for Christ-mas is you,
all I want for Christ-mas is you, ba da ba da ba da ba da ba da ba da ba da ba
all I want for Christ-mas is you, da da da da da da da

68
mp
you, ba - by. All the lights
mp
you, ba - by. oo
mp
da ba da ba da ba da ba da ba da ba oo
mp
da da da da da ba doo ba doo doo doo doo

71
più f
are shin - ing so bright - ly ev - 'ry - where.
oo
oo
and the sour
doo doo doo doo bi doo doo doo doo doo doo doo doo bi doo doo doo doo

75
cresc.
oo
ah
f
and ev - 'ry -
of chil - dren's laugh - ter fills the air.
doo doo doo doo
doo doo doo doo doo doo doo doo doo doo doo doo
ah

79
ff
oh yeah! I hear those sleigh bells ring - ing San-ta won't you bring me the
-one is sing - ing ah yeah
doo doo doo doo ah oh
doo doo doo doo doo doo doo doo San-ta won't you bring me the

83
one I real - ly need, won't you please bring my ba - by to me ee ee
yeah please bring my ba - by to me ee ee oh
f
please bring my ba - by to me ee ee
one I real - ly need, won't you please bring my ba - by to me ee ee

86
f
oo
oo
I don't want a lot for Christ-mas, this is all I'm ask - ing for,
f
I don't want a lot for Christ-mas, this is all I'm ask - ing for, and I
f
doo doo doo doo doo doo doo doo doo doo doo doo doo doo doo doo

90
I just wan-na see my ba-by stand-ing right out-side my door.
I just wan-na see my ba-by stand-ing right out-side my door.
doo doo doo doo doo doo doo doo bi doo doo doo doo doo doo doo doo

94
mf cresc.
I just want you for my own more than you could ev - er know.
oo
oo
doo doo doo doo doo doo doo doo doo doo doo doo doo doo doo doo
98
f
Make my wish come true, ba - by, all I want for Christ - mas

102
ff
is
you,
you,
you,
you,
doo doo doo doo doo doo doo doo doo doo doo doo

106
ba - by,
all I want for Christ - mas is you,
all I want for Chris - mas is you,
you,
you,
ba - by.
doo doo doo doo bi doo doo doo doo bi doo doo doo doo

110
ba - by,
all I want for Christ - mas is
ba - by,
all I want for Chris - mas is
ba - by,
you,
ba - by,
all I want for Christ - mas is

113
you, ba - by, is you.
you, ba - by, is you.
you, ba - by, is you.
you, ba - by, is you.

I SAW MOMMY KISSING SANTA CLAUS

for Greg Beardsell and the Wooburn Singers

Words and music by
TOMMIE CONNOR

arranged by
RICHARD ALLAIN

11
mf
stairs to have a peep. I was tucked up in my bed - room fast a -
stairs to have a peep. I was tucked up in my bed - room fast a -
stairs to have a peep. She thought that I was tucked up in my bed - room fast a -
stairs to have a peep. Tucked up in my bed - room fast a -
16
mf
- sleep. Then I saw Mom-my tick-le San - ta Claus un - der-neath his
- sleep. Then I saw Mom-my tick-le San - ta Claus un - der-neath his
- sleep. Then I saw Mom-my tick-le San - ta Claus un - der-neath his
- sleep. Then I saw Mom-my tick-le San - ta Claus un - der-neath his

22
mp
beard so snow - y white.
Laugh
have been if
mp
beard so snow - y white.
Laugh
have been if
mf
beard so snow - y white.
What a laugh it would have been
if
mp
beard so snow - y white.
Laugh
have been if
27
cresc.
poco rall.
Dad - dy had on - ly seen Mom - my kiss - ing San - ta Claus last
cresc.
Dad - dy had on - ly seen Mom - my kiss - ing San - ta Claus last
cresc.
Dad - dy had on - ly seen Mom - my kiss - ing San - ta Claus last
cresc.
Dad - dy had on - ly seen Mom - my kiss - ing San - ta Claus last

Swing (♩ = 130)
night. I saw Mom-my kiss - ing San - ta Claus,
night. I saw Mom - my, Mom-my kiss - ing San - ta Claus,
night. I saw Mom - my, Mom-my kiss - ing San - ta Claus,
Mer - ry Christ - mas! I saw Mom - my, Mom-my kiss - ing San - ta Claus,
Swing (♩ = 130)
un - der - neath the mis - tle - toe last night, the mis - tle - toe
naugh - ty San - ta, un - der - neath the mis - tle - toe last night, the mis - tle - toe
naugh - ty San - ta, un - der - neath the mis - tle - toe last night, the mis - tle - toe
naugh - ty San - ta, un - der - neath the mis - tle - toe last night, the mis - tle - toe

39
p
_ last night. did - n't hear me, hear me creep, stairs to have a
_ last night. did - n't hear me, hear me creep, stairs to have a
_ last night. did - n't hear me, hear me creep, stairs to have a
_ last night. She did-n't hear_ me creep down the stairs to have a

43
peep. Thought that I was tucked up_ in my bed - room_
peep. She thought that I was tucked up_ in my bed - room_ fast a
peep. Thought that I was tucked up_ in my bed - room_
peep. Thought that I was tucked up_ in my bed - room_

47
mf
Then I saw Mom-my hug - ging San - ta Claus,
mf
-sleep. Then I saw Mom-my, Mom-my hug - ging San - ta Claus,
mf
Then I saw Mom-my, Mom-my hug - ging San - ta Claus,
2nd time only
(snore) (whistle!)
gliss.
mf
zzzzz I saw Mom-my, Mom-my hug - ging San - ta Claus,
51
and San - ta hugged her back right in plain sight.
sau - cy San - ta, San - ta hugged her back right in plain sight, hugged her in
sau - cy San - ta, San - ta hugged her back right in plain sight, hugged her in
sau - cy San - ta, San - ta hugged her back right in plain sight, hugged her in

55
f
What a kick it would have been if Dad-dy had on-ly seen
plain sight. Kick would have been if Dad-dy had on-ly seen
plain sight. Kick would have been if Dad-dy had on-ly seen
plain sight. Kick would have been if Dad-dy had on-ly seen

59
1.
Mom-my kiss-ing San-ta Claus last night. I'm say-in'
Mom-my kiss-ing San-ta Claus last night. I'm say-in'
Mom-my kiss-ing San-ta Claus last night. I'm say-in'
Mom-my kiss-ing San-ta Claus last night. I'm say-in'

64
2.
kiss - ing San - ta Claus, is she the one that he a - dores?
kiss - ing San - ta Claus is she the one that he a - dores?
kiss - ing San - ta Claus is she the one that he a - dores?
kiss - ing San - ta Claus one that he a - dores?
rit.
67
ff
She was kiss - ing San - ta Claus last night.
She was kiss - ing San - ta Claus last night.
She was kiss - ing San - ta Claus last night.
She was kiss - ing San - ta Claus last night.

I WANT A HIPPOPOTAMUS FOR CHRISTMAS

Words and music by
JOHN ROX

arranged by
HYWEL DAVIES

12
SOLO
f
wistful, but becoming increasingly petulant
I want a hip - po - pot - a - mus for Christ - mas.
want a hip - po - pot - a - mus for Christ - mas.
On - ly a hip - po -
Don't think San - ta
p
mm
poco marcato
18
(solo)
-pot - a - mus will do.
Claus will mind, do you?
Don't want a doll, no din - ky Tin - ker
Won't have to use our dir - ty chim - ney
ah

24
(solo)
1.
Toy, want a hip - po - pot - a - mus to play with and en - joy. I
flue, bring him through the front door, that's the eas - y thing to
ah ah ah ah
ah ah
ah ah ah ah

29
2.
(solo)
TUTTI
sotto voce
do. I can see me now on Christ - mas morn - ing, creep - ing down the
ah
sotto voce
See me now I'm creep - ing down the
sotto voce
ah
See me now on Christ - mas morn - ing creep - ing down the
sotto voce
ah
See me now at Christ - mas creep - ing down the

33
sotto voce
stairs. Oh what joy and sur-prise when I o-pen up my eyes to see a hip - po he - ro
cresc.
stairs.
sotto voce
What joy, and a hip - po he - ro
cresc.
stairs.
sotto voce
What joy and sur-prise to see a hip - po he - ro
cresc.
stairs.
sotto voce
What joy, joy and sur-prise a hip - po he - ro
cresc.
37
Allargando (♩ = 54)
f
stand - ing there. I want a hip - po - pot - a - mus for Christ - mas.
f
stand - ing there. I want a hip - po - pot - a - mus for Christ - mas.
f
stand - ing there. I want a hip - po - pot - a - mus for Christ - mas.
f
stand - ing there. I want a hip - po - pot - a - mus for Christ - mas.
Allargando (♩ = 54)

40
rit.
a tempo
On-ly a hip - po - pot - a - mus will do,
no croc - o - diles, no
On-ly a hip - po - pot - a - mus will do,
no croc - o - diles, no
On-ly a hip - po - pot - a - mus will do,
no croc - o - diles, no
On-ly a hip - po - pot - a - mus will do,
no croc - o - diles, no

43
rhi - noc - er - os - es I on - ly like hip - po - pot - a - mus - es, and
rhi - noc - er - os - es I on - ly like hip - po - pot - a - mus - es, and
rhi - noc - er - os - es I on - ly like hip - po - pot - a - mus - es, and
rhi - noc - er - os - es I on - ly like hip - po - pot - a - mus - es, and

46
molto rit.
A tempo (Allargando) (♩ = 54)
hip - po - pot - a - mus - es like me too.
molto legato
hip - po - pot - a - mus - es like me.
mm
molto legato
hip - po - pot - a - mus - es like me.
mm
molto legato
hip - po - pot - a - mus - es like me.
mm
A tempo (Allargando) (♩ = 54)
50
mm
mm
mm
mm
mm
mm

JINGLE BELLS

Words and music by
JAMES PIERPONT

arranged by
RALPH ALLWOOD

* 1st tenor may be sung by altos till bar 12.

5
S.A.
one - horse o - pen sleigh, O'er the fields we go,
T.
one - horse, one - horse, one - horse, one - horse, o'er the fields we go, go, go, go,
B.
one - horse, one - horse, one - horse, one - horse, o'er the fields we go, go, go, go,
7
S.A.
laugh - ing all the way; Bells on bob - tail ring;
T.
laugh - ing all the; ha ha ha ha Bells on bob - tail ding, ding, ding, ding,
B.
laugh - ing all the; ha ha ha ha Bells on bob - tail ding, ding, ding, ding,
9
S.A.
Mak - ing spi - rits bright; What fun it is to ride and sing A
T.
Mak - ing spi - rits; he he he What fun it is to ride and sing A
B.
Mak - ing spi - rits; he he he What fun it is to ride and sing A

11
S.A.
T.
B.
1st x mp 2nd x pp
sleigh - ing song to - night.
Jin - gle bells, jin - gle bells,
13
jin - gle all the way;
Oh, what fun it is to ride in a
15
S.
A.
, f
mp (pp)
one - horse o - pen sleigh. Hey!
Jin - gle bells, jin - gle bells,
Jin - gle, jin - gle
one - horse o - pen sleigh. Hey

17
S.
jin - gle all the way;
Oh, what fun it is to ride in a
A.
all the way;
Oh, what fun it is to ride in a
T.
jin - gle all the way;
Oh, what fun it is to ride in a
all the way;
B.
Jin - gle all the way;
Oh, what fun to

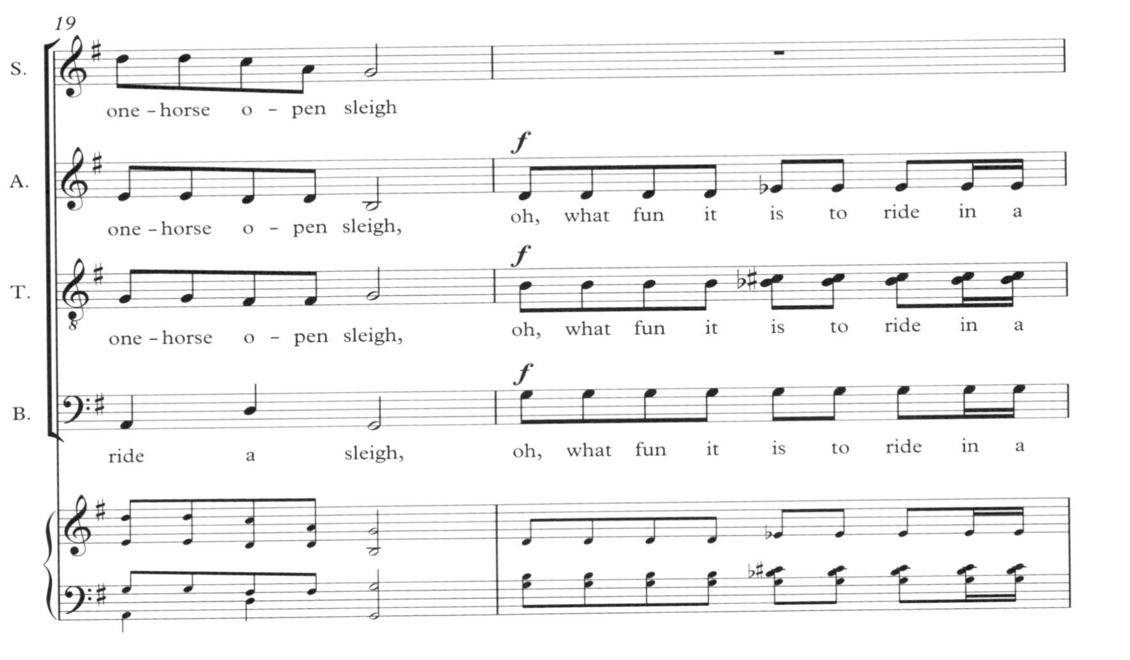
19
S.
one - horse o - pen sleigh
A.
one - horse o - pen sleigh,
f
oh, what fun it is to ride in a
T.
one - horse o - pen sleigh,
f
oh, what fun it is to ride in a
B.
ride a sleigh,
f
oh, what fun it is to ride in a

21
S.
A.
T.
B.
ff
f
Hey!
Now, now, now, now,
one - horse o - pen sleigh. Hey!
Now now, now, now,
one - horse o - pen sleigh. Hey!
one - horse o - pen sleigh. Hey!
Now now, now, now,
23
S.A.
now, now, now, now;
go, go, go, go,
Now the ground is white;
go it while you're young,
now, now, now, now;
go, go, go, go,
25
Take, take, take, take,
sing, sing, sing song.
Take the girls to - night and sing this sleigh - ing song.
Take the girls and sing, sing, sing, song.

27
S.
Get a bob - tailed bay, Two - for - ty for his speed; then
A.
Get a bob - tailed, for - ty speed and
T.
Get a bob - tailed, for - ty speed and
B.
Get a bob - tailed, for - ty speed and

29
S.
hitch him to an o - pen sleigh And crack! you'll take the lead.
A.
hitch him to a take the lead.
T.
hitch him to a take the lead.
B.
hitch him to a sleigh and take the lead.

31
mf
S.
A.
T.
B.
Jin - gle bells, jin - gle bells, jin - gle all the way;

33
S.
A.
T.
B.
Oh, what fun it is to ride in a one-horse o - pen sleigh,

* This shout should be short, loud and high in the voice.

LITTLE SAINT NICK

Words and music by
BRIAN WILSON and MICHAEL LOVE

arranged by
HENRY CAPPER-ALLEN

doo doo doo doo oo do doo doo be do
doo doo doo doo doo doo doo doo do doo doo be do
doo doo doo doo doo doo doo doo Well,
time each year.
oo
dum de dum de dum de dum de do doo doo de
p light
doo doo doo doo doo doo doo doo doo doo doo doo
p light
doo doo doo doo doo doo doo doo doo doo doo doo
way up north where the air gets cold, there's a tale a - bout Christ-mas that you've
lit - tle bob - sled, we call it Old Saint Nick, but she'll walk a to - bog - gan with a
dum de dum de dum de dum dum dum de dum de

14
doo doo doo doo doo doo doo doo doo doo doo doo
doo doo doo doo doo doo doo doo doo doo doo doo
all been told. And a real fa - mous cat all dressed up in red, and he
four - speed stick. She's can - dy ap - ple red with a ski for a wheel, and when
dum de dum de dum de dum de dum de dum dum
17
mp
doo doo doo doo doo doo doo doo oo Lit - tle
mp
doo doo doo doo doo doo doo doo oo Lit - tle
spends the whole year work - in' out on his sled. It's the Lit - tle Saint Nick.
San - ta hits the gas, man, just watch her peel.
doo de doo de
dum da dum da dum da dum da da va da va da va da va

1.
Saint Nick. oo Lit - tle Saint Nick.
Saint Nick. oo Lit - tle Saint Nick.
mf
It's the Lit - tle Saint Nick. Just a
doo Lit - tle Saint Nick. doo de doo de doo Lit - tle Saint Nick.
da va da va da va da va da va da va da va da va da va da va da va da va
2.
mf
Saint Nick. Run, run rein - deer.
mf
Saint Nick. Run, run, rein - deer. A - run, run, rein - deer.
mf
Run, run, rein - deer.
doo Lit - tle Saint Nick.
da va da va da va da va Run, run, rein - deer. A - run, run, rein - deer. A -

26
Run, run, rein - deer. Run, run, rein - deer.
Run, run, rein - deer. A - run, run, rein - deer. Run, run, rein - deer. A
Run, run, rein - deer.
run, run, rein - deer. A - run - a - run - a - run - a - run - a - run, run, rein - deer. A

29
f
Run, run, rein - deer. And
run, run, rein - deer. Run, run, rein - deer.
Run, run, rein - deer.
run, run, rein - deer. A - run, run, rein - deer. He don't miss no - one.

32
haul - in' through the snow at a fright-'nin' speed,_ with a half a doz - en deer, with a
f
Haul - in' through the snow at a fright-'nin' speed,_ with a half a do - zen deer, with a
f
da va va da va a fright-'nin' speed_ va da va da va va da va a
f
da va va da va a fright-'nin' speed_ va da va da va va da va a
35
Ru - dy to lead._ He's got - ta wear his gog-gles 'cause the snow real - ly flies,_ and he's
Ru - dy to lead._ He's got - ta wear his gog-gles 'cause the snow real - ly flies,_ and he's
Ru - dy to lead._ va da va da va va da va the snow real - ly flies,_ va da va
Ru - dy to lead._ va da va da va va da va the snow real - ly flies,_ va da va

38
cruis - in' ev - 'ry pad with a lit - tle sur - prise. It's the Lit - tle Saint Nick.
mf
cruis - in' ev - 'ry pad with a lit - tle sur - prise. oo Lit - tle
mf
da va va da va a lit - tle sur - prise. oo Lit - tle
mf
doo de doo de
da va va da va a lit - tle sur - prise. da va da va da va da va
41
3
It's the Lit - tle Saint Nick. ah
Saint Nick, oo Lit - tle Saint Nick. ah
Saint Nick, oo Lit - tle Saint Nick. ah
doo Lit - tle Saint Nick, doo de doo de doo Lit - tle Saint Nick.
da va da va da va da va da va da va da va da va da va da va da va da va
3

44
Mer - ry Christ - mas Saint Nick.
Mer - ry Christ - mas Saint Nick. oo
Mer - ry Christ - mas Saint Nick. oo
da de da de Mer - ry Christ - mas. Christ - mas comes this
da va da va da va da va Mer - ry Christ - mas Saint Nick. da da dum da
47
ah
Mer - ry Christ - mas Saint
ah
Mer - ry Christ - mas Saint
ah
Mer - ry Christ - mas Saint
time each year. da de da de Mer - ry Christ - mas.
da dum da da da da va da va da va da va Mer - ry Christ - mas Saint

50
Nick.
ah
Nick.
oo
ah
Nick.
oo
ah
f
Christ - mas comes this time each year.
da de da de
Nick. da da dum da da dum da da da
da va da va da va da va
53
f
Mer - ry Christ - mas Saint Nick.
p
oo
f
Mer - ry Christ - mas Saint Nick.
p
oo
f
Mer - ry Christ - mas Saint Nick.
p
oo
f
Mer - ry Christ - mas. Christ - mas comes this time each year.
p
oo
Mer - ry Christ - mas Saint Nick.
oo

MISTLETOE AND WINE

LESLIE STEWART and JEREMY PAUL

KEITH STRACHAN
arranged by TOM RECKNELL

13
dim.
mp
fin - gers numb, fac - es a - glow. It's Christ - mas time, mis - tle - toe and wine.
dim.
mp
ah fac - es a - glow. It's Christ - mas time, mis - tle - toe and wine.
dim.
mp
ah fac - es a - glow. It's Christ - mas time, mis - tle - toe and wine.
dim.
mp
ah fac - es a - glow. It's Christ - mas time, mis - tle - toe and wine.
21
cresc.
mf
Child - ren sing - ing Chris - ti - an rhyme; with logs on the fire and gifts on the
cresc.
mf
Child - ren sing - ing Chris - ti - an rhyme; with logs on the fire and gifts on the
cresc.
mf
Child - ren sing - ing Chris - ti - an rhyme; with logs on the fire and gifts on the
cresc.
mf
Child - ren sing - ing Chris - ti - an rhyme; with logs on the fire and gifts on the

28
dim.
mp
tree, a time to re - joice in the good that we see. A time for
tree, oo good that we see. A time for
tree, oo good that we see. A time for
tree, oo in the good that we see. A time for
34
liv - ing, a time for be - liev - ing, a time for trust - ing, not de - ceiv - ing.
liv - ing, time for be - liev - ing, time for trust - ing, not de - ceiv - ing.
liv - ing, time for be - liev - ing, time for trust - ing, not de - ceiv - ing.
liv - ing, time for be - liev - ing, time for trust - ing, not de - ceiv - ing.

41
cresc.
mf
dim.
mp
Love and laugh - ter and joy ev - er af - ter. Ours for the tak-ing, just
ah
Ours for the tak-ing, just
pp
47
fol - low the mas - ter.
Christ - mas time, mis-tle-toe and wine.

53
cresc.
mp
Child - ren sing - ing Chris - ti - an rhyme. With logs on the fire and gifts on the tree, a
cresc.
mp
Child - ren sing - ing Chris - ti - an rhyme. oo
cresc.
mp
Child - ren sing - ing Chris - ti - an rhyme. oo
cresc.
mp
Child - ren sing - ing Chris - ti - an rhyme. oo
61
dim.
p
cresc.
time to re-joice in the good that we see. A time for giv-ing, a time for
dim.
p
cresc.
mm
ah
dim.
p
cresc.
mm
ah
dim.
p
cresc.
mm
ah

69
mf cresc.
get-ting, a time for for-giv-ing, and for for-get-ting. Christ-mas is love,
is love,
is love,
is love,
76
poco f
f
Christ-mas is peace. Time for hat-ing and fight-ing to cease. Christ-mas time,
is peace. oo ah Christ-mas time,
is peace. oo ah Christ-mas time,
is peace. oo ah Christ-mas time,

84
mis-tle-toe and wine. Child - ren sing - ing Chris - ti - an rhyme; with logs on the
mis-tle-toe and wine. Child - ren sing - ing Chris - ti - an rhyme; with logs on the
mis-tle-toe and wine. Child - ren sing - ing Chris - ti - an rhyme; with logs on the
mis-tle-toe and wine. Child - ren sing - ing Chris - ti - an rhyme; with logs on the
91
dim.
rit.
mp
fire and gifts on the tree, time to re - joice in the good that we see.
fire and gifts on the tree, time to re - joice in the good that we see.
fire and gifts on the tree, time to re - joice in the good that we see.
fire and gifts on the tree, time to re - joice in the good that we see.

NEVER DO A TANGO WITH AN ESKIMO

Words and music by
TOMMIE CONNOR

arranged by
MATTHEW O'DONOVAN

mp
sim.
doo doo doo doo doo doo doo doo doo doo doo doo
nev-er do a tan-go with an Es-ki-mo! No, no, no! Oh dear, no! When a
legato
oo
wah
f
doo-wah
la-dy from Ne-bras-ka's at a par-ty in A-las ka she must nev-er do a tan-go with an Es-ki-mo!
mf
doo-wah You can

17
mp
doo doo doo
doo doo doo
doo doo doo
doo doodoo
doo doo_ doo doo doo_ doo doo doo_ doo doo doo_
doo doo_ doo doo doo_ doo doo doo_ doo doo doo_ Bu
do it with a La-tin from Man-il-la to Man hat tan, you can do it with a gau-cho in Bra-zil.
21
mp
f
ah
You can bet your life you're gon-na get a
once those Es-ki-mos-es start to wig-gle with their toes-es, you can bet your life you're gon-na get a

4
Brrr!
mp
sim.
chill!
doo doo doo doo doo doo
mf
chill! You must nev - er do a tan - go with an Es - ki - mo!
chill!
chill, get a chill!
legato
7
doo doo doo doo doo doo
oo
No! No! No! Oh dear, no! If you do you'll get the breeze up and you'll

30
wah
doo-wah
end up with a freeze up. You must nev-er do a tan-go with an Es - ki - mo!
wah
doo-wah
doo doo doo wah
doo-wah
33
No, no, no, no! No, no, no, no, no! Nev-er do a tan-go with an
No, no, no, no! No, no, no, no, no! Nev-er do a tan-go with an
No, no, no, no, no! ba ba-ya ba
No, no, no, no, no, no, no, no, no!
ba ba-ya ba

6
Es - ki - mo, nev - er, no, nev - er, no, nev - er, no, nev - er, no,
Es - ki - mo, nev - er, no, nev - er, no, nev - er, no, nev - er, no
sim.
ba ba - ya ba ba ba - ya ba
sim.
ba ba - ya ba ba ba - ya ba
8
no, no, no! ba ba ba ba ba ba ba-de-la-de-la
no, no, no! ba ba ba ba ba ba ba ba ba
ba ba - ya ba ba ba-ya ba ba ba-ya ba
ba ba - ya ba ba ba-ya ba ba ba-ya ba

pp
mp leggero
No, no, no, no, no, no! You must nev-er do a tan - go with an Es - ki - mo!
No, no, no, no, no, no! oo doo doo doo doo doo doo
sim.
ba oo doo doo doo doo doo doo
ba oo doo doo doo doo doo doo
No, no, no! Oh dear, no! oo
doo doo doo doo doo When a la-dy from Ne-bras-ka's at a par-ty in A-las-ka she m
espress.
doo ah doo doo oo
doo doo doo doo doo doo oo

brillante
f
wah
doo-wah ba ba ba
ba ba ba ba ba
ne-ver do a tan-go with an Es - ki - mo!
ba ba ba ba ba
wah
doo-wah ba ba ba
ba ba ba ba ba
wah
doo-wah ba ba ba
ba ba-ya ba
ba da ba ba
ba da ba da ba da ba da ba da ba da
ba de la
When a
sim.
ba ba ba ba ba
ba ba ba ba ba
ba ba
ba ba ba ba ba
ba ba ba ba ba
ba ba
ba ba-ya ba
ba ba - ya ba
ba ba-ya

55
la - dy from Ne - bra - ska's at a par - ty in A - las - ka she must ne - ver do a tan - go with an
ah
ah
ah
doo doo doo
58
mp
Es - ki - mo!
oo
mp
oo
doo doo doo
mp
mf
doo-wah
doo doo doo doo
You can do it with A - pa - ches in P
mf
meno f
doo doo-wah You can do it with a sai - lor from Pe - ru to Ven - e - zue - la,
doo doo-wah ba

62
mf
But if once an Es - ki - mo - see starts to cud - dle up so co - sy, you will
oo
oo
You will
- ree.
oo
Oh, you will
ah
oo
You will
65
gliss.
ff
find your pas - sion cool - ing, yes sir - ee! (ah)
Nev - er do a tan - go with an
find your pas - sion cool - ing, yes sir - ee! (ah)
Nev - er do a tan - go with an
find your pas - sion cool - ing, yes sir - ee! (ah)
Nev - er do a tan - go with an
find your pas - sion cool - ing, yes sir - ee! (ah)
ba ba - ya ba

68
Es - ki - mo, tan - go with an Es - ki - mo. Oh,
Es - ki mo, no, no no! Oh dear no! If you do you'll get the breeze up and you
Es - ki - mo, tan - go with an Es - ki - mo. ba ba - ya ba
[a few first basses in falsetto]
Brrr!
sim.
ba ba ya ba ba ba-ya ba ba ba ya ba ba ba - ya ba
72
Oh, ba - ya
end up with a freeze up. You must ne - ver do a tan - go with an Es - ki - mo.
ba ba - ya ba ba a tan - go with an Es - ki - mo.
ba ba - ya ba ba doo doo doo doo ba - ya

75
mf
meno f
Oh, nev - er do a tan - go with an
No, no, no, no, no, no, no, no, no! Nev - er do a tan - go with an
Oh, no! With an
Oh, no!
78
ff
mf
pp
Es - ki - mo. Oh!
Es - ki - mo. Oh!
(solo, spoken)
tutti
f
Es - ki - mo. No, no no! Oh!
No, no, no, no, no, no, no, no, no! No, no, no! Oh, no!

SANTA BABY

for Jim Davey and Chantage

Words and music by
JOAN JAVITS, PHIL and TONY SPRINGER

arranged by
RICHARD ALLAIN

for me.
Been an aw - ful good girl,
San - ta, ba by,
San - ta, ba - by,
so
boom ba boom ba boom ba boom ba boom ba boom ba boom ba
hur - ry.
mf
boo boo boo boo
click
hur - ry down the chim - ney to - night.
boom boom ba boom ba boom ba boom ba boom ba

13
San - ta, ba - by, a fif - ty - four con - ver - ti - ble too, light blue.
San - ta, ba - by, a fif - ty - four con - ver - ti - ble too, light blue.
mf
San - ta, ba - by, a fif - ty - four con - ver - ti - ble too, light blue.
San - ta, ba - by, a fif - ty - four con - ver - ti - ble too, light blue.
boom ba boom ba boom ba boom ba boom ba boom ba boom ba
16
I'll wait up for you, dear, San - ta, ba - by, hur - ry,
I'll wait up for you, dear, San - ta, ba - by, hur - ry,
I'll wait up for you, dear, San - ta, ba - by, so hur - ry down the chim - ney to - night
I'll wait up for you, dear, San - ta, ba - by, hur - ry
boom ba boom ba boom ba boom ba boom ba boom

9
p
San - ta, hur - ry down the chim - ney to - night. oo
p
San - ta, hur - ry down the chim - ney to - night. oo
p
hur - ry down the chim - ney to - night. oo
mf
San - ta, hur - ry down the chim - ney to - night. Think of all the
p
boom bom bom bom bom bom bom
2
fun I've missed, oo that I have - n't kissed.
mf
fun I've missed, Think of all the fel - las that I have - n't kissed.
fun I've missed, oo that I have - n't kissed.
p
fun I've missed, oo that I have - n't kissed.
bom ba dom bom bom bom bom bom bom bom ba dom bom bom

25
oo just as good if you Christ-mas list.
p
oo just as good if you Christ-mas list.
mf
Next year I could be just as good if you Christ-mas list.
oo just as good if you Christ-mas list.
mf
bom bom bom bom bom if you check off my Christ-mas list. ba boom
29
mf
San - ta, ba - by, I want a yacht and real - ly that's not a lot.
mf
San - ta, ba - by, I want a yacht and real - ly that's not a lot.
mf
San - ta, ba - by, I want a yacht and real - ly that's not a lot.
mf
San - ta, ba - by, I want a yacht and real - ly that's not a lot.
boom ba boom ba boom ba boom ba boom ba boom ba boom ba

32
Been an an - gel this year, San - ta, ba - by, hur - ry,
Been an an - gel this year, San - ta, ba - by, hur - ry,
Been an an - gel this year, San - ta, ba - by, so hur - ry down the chim - ney to - night.
Been an an - gel this year, San - ta, ba - by, hur - ry,
boom ba boom ba boom ba boom ba boom ba hur - ry down the chim - ney to - night.
35
San - ta, hur - ry down the chim - ney to - night. boo boo
San - ta, hur - ry down the chim - ney to - night. boo boo
hur - ry down the chim - ney to - night. boom ba boom ba
San - ta, hur - ry down the chim - ney to - night. boo boo
to - night. San - ta, ba - by, one

38
boo boo boo boo boo boo
boom ba boom ba boom ba boom ba boom ba boom ba boom ba boom ba
ossia
lit - tle thing
lit - tle thing I real - ly need, the deed to a pla - ti - num mine,
see ossia
41
boo boo hurry,
down the chim - ney,
hur - ry,
boom ba boom ba hur - ry,
San - ta, ba - by, so hur - ry down the chim - ney to - night,
mf

4
click
hur - ry to - night.
hur - ry to - night.
mf
hur - ry to - night.
San - ta, cu - tie, and fill my stock - ing with a du - plex
hur - ry to - night.
mf
ba boom ba boom
ba boom ba
7
p
San - ta, cu - tie, San - ta, cu - tie, San - ta, cu - tie,
p
San - ta, cu - tie, San - ta, cu - tie, San - ta, cu - tie,
and cheques, sign your X on the line, San - ta, cu - tie, and
p
San - ta, cu - tie, San - ta, cu - tie, San - ta, cu - tie,
boom ba boom ba boom ba boom ba boom ba boom ba boom ba

50
f
hur - ry,
San - ta, won't you hur - ry down the chim-ney to - night?
hur - ry,
San - ta, won't you hur - ry down the chim-ney to - night?
hur - ry down the chim-ney to - night,
won't you hur - ry down the chim-ney to - night?
hur - ry,
San - ta, won't you hur - ry down the chim-ney to - night?
mf
boom
boom
bom bom
53
Come and trim my Christ-mas tree,
with some dec - o - ra - tions bought at
Come and trim my Christ-mas tree,
with some dec - o - ra - tions bought at
Come and trim my Christ-mas tree,
with some dec - o - ra - tions bought at
Come and trim my Christ-mas tree,
with some dec - o - ra - tions bought at
bom bom bom bom Christ-mas tree bom bom

56
f
Tif - fa - ny. I real - ly do be - lieve in you,
Tif - fa - ny. I real - ly do be - lieve in you,
Tif - fa - ny. I real - ly do be - lieve in you,
Tif - fa - ny. I real - ly do be - lieve in you,
dom bom bom bom bom bom bom bom
59
let's be - lieve in me. Santa, baby, for -
let's be - lieve in me. San - ta, ba - by, for -
let's see if you be - lieve in me. San - ta, ba - by, for -
let's be - lieve in me. San - ta, ba - by, for -
let's ba boom ba boom ba boom ba

62
got to men - tion one lit - tle thing, a ring.
got to men - tion one lit - tle thing, a ring.
got to men - tion one lit - tle thing, a ring.
got to men - tion one lit - tle thing, a ring.
boom ba boom ba boom ba boom ba boom ba

64
I don't mean on the phone, San - ta, ba - by,
I don't mean on the phone, San - ta, ba - by,
I don't mean on the phone, San - ta, ba - by,
I don't mean on the phone, San - ta, ba - by, so
boom ba boom ba boom ba boom ba boom ba

66
mf
[optional solo]
hur - ry,
I'll be wait - ing,
hur - ry down the chim - ney to - night.
hur - ry,
I'll be wait - ing,
hur - ry,
I'll be wait - ing,
hur - ry down the chim - ney to - night.
I'll be wait - ing,
click
boom
69
[tutti]
mp
an - tic - i - pat - ing,
an - tic - i - pat - ing,
[optional solo]
an - tic - i - pat - ing,
hur - ry down the chim - ney to - night.
an - tic - i - pat - ing,

71
San - ta, won't you hur - ry,
San - ta, ba - by,
[tutti]
Won't you hur - ry,
[optional solo]
hur - ry down the chim - ney to - night.
74
hur - ry
down the chim - ney to - night?
mm
[tutti]
Hur - ry

SEE AMID THE WINTER'S SNOW

Words by
EDWARD CASWALL

JOHN GOSS
arranged by MATTHEW O'DONOVAN

12
tutti
mf
ter - nal years. Hail, thou ev - er - bles - sed morn. Hail, re-demp-tion's
mf
Hail, thou ev - er - bles - sed morn. Hail, re-demp-tion's
mf
Hail, thou ev - er - bles - sed morn. Hail, re-demp-tion's
mf
Hail, thou ev - er - bles - sed morn. Hail, re-demp-tion's
8vb

16
hap - py dawn. Sing through all Je - ru - sa - lem, Christ is born in Beth - le -
hap - py dawn. Sing through all Je - ru - sa - lem, Christ is born in Beth - le -
hap - py dawn. Sing through all Je - ru - sa - lem, Christ is born in Beth - le -
hap - py dawn. Sing through all Je - ru - sa - lem, Christ is born in Beth - le -

21
Swing (♩ = 132)
-hem.
-hem.
-hem.
-hem.
Swing (♩ = 132)
f
senza ped.
3
3
25
mp
Lo, with-in a man - ger lies
He who built the star - ry skies.
mp
Lo, with-in a man - ger lies
He who built the star - ry skies.
8va
(quasi pizz)
mp
mp
29
He who, throned in height sub - lime,
sits a - mid the cher - u - bim.
He who, throned in height sub - lime,
sits a - mid the cher - u - bim.
3

33
Hail, thou ev - er - bles - sed morn.
Hail, redemp - tion's
Hail, thou ev - er - bles - sed morn.
Hail, re - demp - tion's
Hail, thou ev - er - bles - sed morn.
Hail, re - demp - tion's
Hail, thou ev - er - bles sed morn.
Hail, re - demp - tion's
Ped.

36
hap - py dawn.
Sing through all Je - ru - sa - lem,
Christ is born in
hap - py dawn.
Sing through all Je - ru - sa - lem,
Christ is born in
hap - py dawn.
Sing through all Je - ru - sa - lem,
Christ is born in
hap - py dawn.
Sing through all Je - ru - sa - lem,
Christ is born in

Beth - le - hem.
Beth - le - hem.
Beth - le - hem.
Beth - le - hem.
f
4
mp
Say, ye ho - ly shep - herds, say what your joy - ful
mp dolce
mp
8
news to - day. Where - fore have ye left your sheep, on the lone - ly
mp
Where - fore have ye left your sheep, on the
mp
Where - fore have ye left your sheep, on the

52
f
moun-tain steep? Hail, thou ev - er - bles - sed morn. Hail, re - demp - tion's
moun-tain steep? Hail, thou ev - er - bles - sed morn. Hail, re - demp - tion's
moun-tain steep? Hail, thou ev - er - bles - sed morn. Hail, re - demp - tion's
moun-tain steep? Hail, thou ev - er - bles - sed morn. Hail, re - demp - tion's
ff
Ped.

56
hap - py dawn. Sing through all Je - ru - sa - lem, Christ is born in
hap - py dawn. Sing through all Je - ru - sa - lem, Christ is born in
hap - py dawn. Sing through all Je - ru - sa - lem, Christ is born in
hap - py dawn. Sing through all Je - ru - sa - lem, Christ is born in
(improv. ad lib.)
8va

60
Beth - le - hem.
Beth - le - hem.
Beth - le - hem.
Beth - le - hem.
f

64
mf
A won-drous
p
mf
Dead of night
a won-drous
p
mf
Dead of night
a won-drous
mp
cresc. molto
As we watched at dead of night,
lo, we saw a won-drous light.
p
cresc.

69
light. "Peace on earth", of the Sa-viour's birth.
light. "Peace on earth", of the Sa-viour's birth.
light. "Peace on earth", of the Sa-viour's birth.
f
An - gels sing-ing, "Peace on earth", told us of the Sa-viour's birth.
mf
f
8vb

73
ff
Hail thou ev - er - bles-sed morn. Hail, re-demp - tion's hap - py dawn.
ff
Hail thou ev - er - bles-sed morn. Hail, re-demp - tion's hap - py dawn.
ff
Hail thou ev - er - bles-sed morn. Hail, re-demp - tion's hap - py dawn.
ff
Hail thou ev - er - bles-sed morn. Hail, re-demp - tion's hap - py dawn.
ff
(8)
Ped. *

77
mf
Sing_ through all Je - ru - sa - lem,_ Christ_ is born in Beth - le -
mf
Sing_ through all Je - ru - sa - lem,_ Christ_ is born in Beth - le -
mf
Sing_ through all Je - ru - sa - lem,_ Christ_ is born in Beth - le -
mf
Sing_ through all Je - ru - sa - lem,_ Christ_ is born in Beth - le -
(ad lib.)
81
Poco meno mosso
(straight rhythm)
-hem.
p
oo
-hem.
p
oo
-hem.
mp
Teach, O teach us, Ho - ly Child, by thy face so
-hem.
p
oo
Poco meno mosso
(straight rhythm)
f

86
poco cresc.
(oo)
poco cresc.
(oo)
poco cresc.
meek and mild, teach us to re - sem - ble thee, in thy sweet hu - mil - i - ty:
poco cresc.
(oo)
3
8vb

Swing (♩ = 132)
91
ff
Hail, thou ev - er - bles-sed morn. Hail, re - demp - tion's hap - py dawn.
ff
Hail, thou ev - er - bles-sed morn. Hail, re - demp - tion's hap - py dawn.
ff
Hail, thou ev - er - bles-sed morn. Hail, re - demp - tion's hap - py dawn.
ff
Hail, thou ev - er - bles-sed morn. Hail, re - demp - tion's hap - py dawn.
Swing (♩ = 132)
ff
3
3
3
(8)
Ped.
*

95
f
Sing_ through all Je - ru - sa-lem,_ Christ_ is born in Beth - le-hem._
(ad lib.)
8vb

99
ff
Hail,_ thou ev - er - bles - sed morn._ Hail,_ re - demp - tion's
(8)
Ped.
*

102
hap - py dawn.
Sing through all Je - ru - sa - lem,
hap - py dawn.
Sing through all Je - ru - sa - lem,
hap - py dawn.
Sing through all Je - ru - sa - lem,
hap - py dawn.
Sing through all Je - ru - sa - lem,

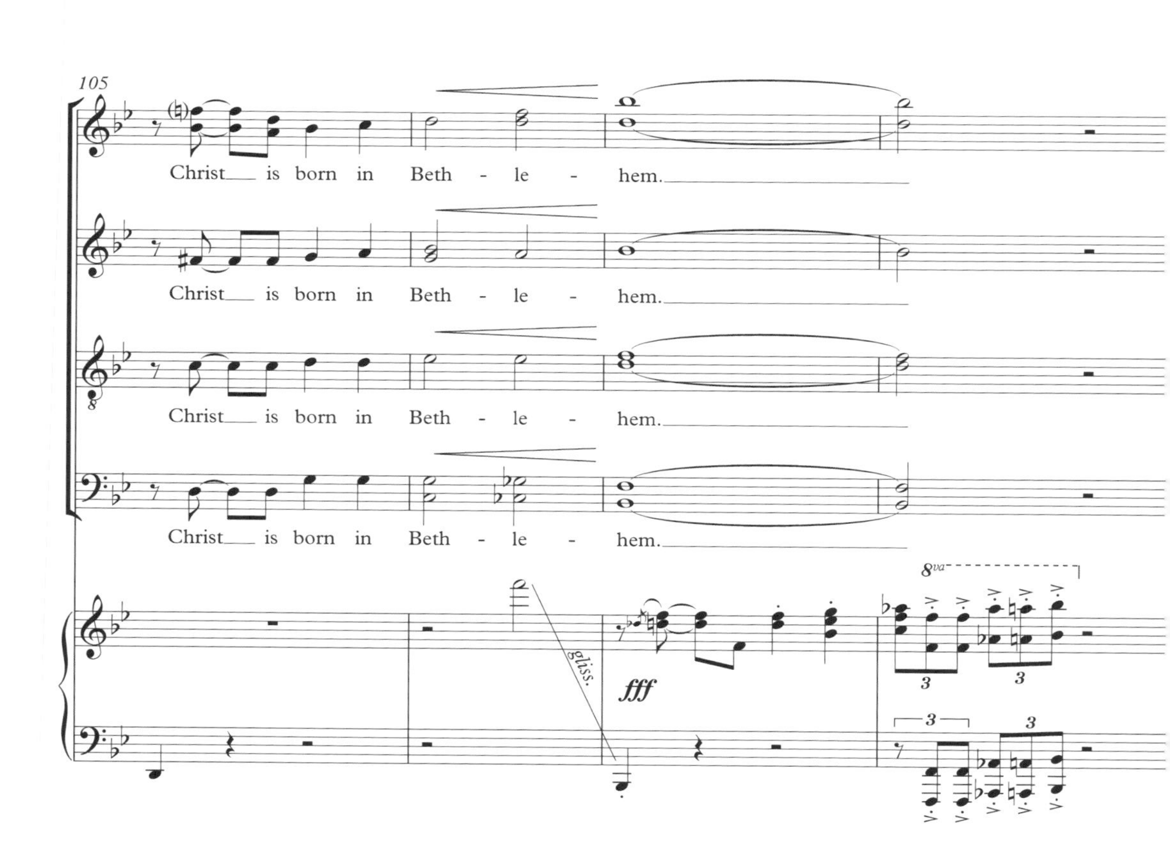
105
Christ is born in Beth - le - hem.
Christ is born in Beth - le - hem.
Christ is born in Beth - le - hem.
Christ is born in Beth - le - hem.
gliss.
fff
8va

WE WISH YOU A MERRY CHRISTMAS

Traditional words

Traditional melody
arranged by JOHN GARDNER

15
cresc.
mf p
and your kin, we wish you a mer-ry Christ - mas and a hap - py new
you to you and your kin, mer - ry Christ - mas and a hap -
and your kin, and a hap -
bring to you, to you and your kin, and a hap - py new
cresc.
mf p

20
Year.
- py new Year.
- py new Year.
SOLO (T. or B.)
mf
Year.
1. Now bring us some fig-gy
p
26
pud - ding, now bring us some fig - gy pud - ding, now bring us some fig - gy pud - ding and
mf
3

31
S.
A.
p
and your kin, we
cresc.
Good ti - dings we bring to you to you and your
(solo)
tutti
T.
B.
p
and your
bring some out here.
Good ti -dings we bring to you, to
cresc.
p
37
mf
p
wish you a mer-ry Christ - mas and a hap - py new Year.
kin, mer - ry Christ-mas and a hap - - py new Year.
kin, and a hap - - py new Year.
you and your kin, and a hap - py new Year.
mf
p
p
42
SOLO (T. or B.)
mf
2. For we all like fig-gy pud - ding, for we
mf

47
all like fig-gy pud - ding, for we all like fig-gy pud - ding, so bring some out
52
S.
A.
p
and your kin, we
cresc.
Good tid - ings we bring to you to you and your
(solo)
p
tutti
T.
p
and your
here.
B.
Good tid - ings we bring to you, to
cresc.
p
57
mf p
wish you a mer - ry Christ - mas and a hap - py new Year.
kin, mer - ry Christ - mas and a hap - - py new Year.
kin, and a hap - - py new Year.
you and your kin, and a hap - py new Year.
mf p
p

62
S.
f
3. And we won't go till we've got some, till
A.
f
And we won't go till we've
T.
f
And we
B.
cresc.
f
68
we've got some, and we won't go til we've got some, so
got some, till we've got some, so bring some out
won't go till we've got some, till we've got some, so
f
And we won't go till we've got some, so bring some

72
ff
bring some out here. Good tid-ings we bring, we wish
here. Good tid - ings we bring to you and your kin, we
bring some out here. Good tid-ings we bring, we wish
out here. Good tid - ings we bring to you and your kin, to
78
rall. un poco
pp
p
you a mer-ry Christ - mas and a hap - py new Year.
wish you a mer-ry Christ - mas and a ha - py new Year.
you a mer-ry Christ - mas and a ha - py new Year.
you and your kin, and a ha - py new Year.
8va
senza Ped.

WHEN SANTA GOT STUCK UP THE CHIMNEY

Words and music by
JIMMY GRAFTON

arranged by
JONATHAN WIKELEY

Gently

SOPRANO *p*
do do do do do do do do do

ALTO *p*
do do do do do do do do do do

TENOR *mp*
do do do do do do do do do do do do do do do do do

BARITONE *p*
do do do do do do do do do do do do do do do do

BASS *p*
do do do do do do do do do do

Gently

Rehearsal accompaniment

6

do do do do do do

do do do do *p* do do do do do do do do

do do do do do do do do do do do do do do do do

do do do do do do do do do do do do

do do do do do do do do do do

12
mp
When San-ta got stuck up the chim - ney, he be-gan to
do do do do do do do He be-gan to
do do do do do do do He be-gan to,
do do do do do do do He be-gan to
do do do do do do do do do do do do He be-gan to
16
shout, "You girls and boys won't get a - ny toys, if you don't pull me
shout, do do do do do do if you don't pull me
'gan to shout, do do do do do if you don't pull me
shout, do do do do do do if you, you don't
shout, do do do do do do if you don't pull

out. My beard is black, there's soot in my sack, my nose is tick - (e)l - ing
out. do do nose is
out. do do nose is
pull me out. do do do nose is
me out. do do do
too." When San-ta got stuck up the chim - ney, a - choo, a-choo - choo - choo
tick - ling too do do chim - ney, a - choo - choo - choo - choo -
tick - ling do do chim - ney, a - choo - choo, a - choo, a-choo -
tick - ling do do chim - ney, a - choo choo choo choo, a -
do do do chim - ney, a - choo - choo - choo - choo -

29
mp
ah
mp
-choo - choo
ah
mp
-choo - choo
ah
mf
-choo, a-choo. 'Twas on the eve be - fore Christ-mas Day, when San - ta Claus ar -
-choo - choo
33
mf
And in - to a chim-ney he climbed with his sack, but he was so fat he
ah
mp
-rived on his sleigh,
ah
mp
ah
ba da

7
Oh what a ter - ri - ble plight, he stayed up there all night.
could - n't get back. Oh what a ter - ri - ble plight, he stayed up there all night.
Oh what a ter - ri - ble plight, he stayed up there all night.
Oh what a ter - ri - ble plight, he stayed up there all night.
ba da Oh what a ter - ri - ble plight, he stayed up there all night.
12
mp
When
p
do do do do do do do do do do do
p
do do do do do do do do do do do
p
do do do do do do do do do do do
p
do do do do do do do do do do do

46
San-ta got stuck up the chim - ney,_ he be-gan to yell, "Oh
mp
do do do do do do do do do do do do do
do do_ do do_ he be-gan to, 'gan_ to yell,_
do do_ do do do_ he be-gan to yell, do_ do d
do do_ do do_ do do do he be-gan to yell, do_
50
hur - ry please,_ it's oh, such a squeeze,_ the rein-deer's stuck as well. His
p
do do_ do the_ rein-deer's stuck as well.
mp
do do do do do do the rein-deer's stuck as well._
do do_ do the_ rein - deer's_ stuck, stuck as well.
do do_ do do do_ the rein - deer's_ stuck as well._

4
head's up there in the cold night air, now Ru-dolph's nose is blue." When
do do Ru - dolph's nose is
p
do do Ru - dolph's nose is
do do do Ru - doph's nose is
do do do is
3
8
San - ta got stuck up the chim - ney, a - choo, a - choo - choo - choo
blue do do chim - ney, a - choo - choo - choo - choo -
do do chim - ney, a - choo - choo, a - choo, a - choo -
do do chim - ney, a - choo choo choo choo, a -
blue do chim - ney, a - choo - choo - choo - choo -

62
mf
-choo - choo. Then Ru - dolph tugged with all of his might, but San - ta Claus was
-choo - choo. Then Ru - doph tugged with all of his might, but San - ta Claus was
-choo, a-choo. Then Ru - dolph tugged with all of his might, but San - ta Claus was
-choo - choo. Then Ru - dolph tugged with all of his might, but San - ta Claus was
-choo - choo.
66
stuck ve - ry tight, he wig - gled and jig - gled then cried with a frown, "I'll
stuck ve - ry tight, he wrig - gled and jig - gled then cried with a frown, "I'll
stuck ve - ry tight, he wig - gled and jig - gled then cried with a frown, "I'll
stuck ve - ry tight, he wig - gled and jig - gled then cried with a frown, "I'll
He wrig - gled and jig - gled then cried with a frown, "I'll

69
nev - er get up, I'll nev - er get down, oh what a ter - ri - ble fuss, we
nev - er get up, I'll nev - er get down, oh what a ter - ri - ble fuss, we
nev - er get up, I'll nev - er get down, oh what a ter - ri - ble fuss, we
nev - er get up, I'll nev - er get down, oh what a ter - ri - ble fuss, we
nev - er get up, I'll nev - er get down, oh what a ter - ri - ble fuss, we
73
should have come by bus."
should have come by bus." do do do do do do do do
should have come by bus." do do do do do do do do
should have come by bus." do do do do do do do
should have come by bus." do do do do do do

78
mp
When San-ta got stuck up the chim - ney,
he be-gan to
do do do do do do do do do do do do do do
do do do do do do do
he be-gan to,
do do do do do do do
he be-gan to
do do do do do do do do do do do do he be-gan to
82
shout, "You girls and boys won't get a - ny toys if you don't pull me
p
do do do do do do if you don't pull me
-gan to shout
do do do do do do if you don't pull me
shout, do do do do do do if you, you don't
shout, do do do do do do do if you don't pull

86
out, my beard is black, there's soot in my sack, my nose is tick-(e)l-ing
out, do do nose is
out, do do nose is
pull me out, do do do nose is
me out, do do do
3
90
dim.
too." When San-ta got stuck up the chim-ney, a-choo, a choo-
tick-ling too, do do chim-ney, a-choo-choo-
tick-ling do do chim-ney, a-choo-choo a-
tick-ling do do chim-ney, a-choo-choo-
do do do chim-ney, a-choo-choo-

94
- choo - choo - choo - choo - choo - choo, a - choo, a - choo,
- choo - choo - choo - choo, a - choo, a - choo - choo, a - choo,
- choo, a - choo - choo - choo, a - choo - choo - choo - choo, a -
- choo - choo, a - choo, a - choo - choo, a - choo - choo -
- choo - choo - choo - choo - choo - choo - choo, a - choo -
98
ppp
a - choo - choo - choo, a - choo!
ppp
a - choo - choo - choo, a - choo!
ppp
- choo, a - choo - choo - choo, a - choo!
ff
- choo - choo a - choo, a - choo, a - choo!
ppp
- choo - choo - choo - choo, a - choo!

WONDERFUL CHRISTMASTIME

Words and music by
PAUL McCARTNEY

arranged by
BERTY RICE

13
S.
A.
T.
B.
dim.
ba ba ba da ba be doo wah
ba ba ba da ba be doo wah
be doo wah
ba ba ba da ba doo wah
doo doo doo doo doo doo wah
doo doo doo doo doo doo wah ba doot
17
mp
doo doo wah wah wah wah wah wah doo doo wah wah wah wah wah wah
doo doo wah wah wah wah wah wah doo doo wah wah wah wah wah wah
The mood is right, the spi-rit's up,
doo doo wah wah wah wah wah wah doo doo wah wah wah wah wah wah
The mood is right, the spi-rit's up,
doo tch tch tch ba doot doo tch tch tch ba doot

21
S.
doo doo wah wah wah wah wah wah doo doo wah wah wah wah wah wah
A.
doo doo wah wah wah wah wah wah doo doo wah wah wah wah wah wah
We're here to - night, and that's e - nough.
T.
doo doo wah wah wah wah wah wah doo doo wah wah wah wah wah wah
B.
We're here to - night, and that's e - nough.
doo tch tch tch ba doo doo tch tch ba doo doo doo doo
25
S.
Sim - ply hav - ing a won - der - ful Christ - mas time,
A.
Sim - ply hav - ing a won - der - ful Christ - mas time,
T.
Sim - ply hav - ing a won - der - ful Christ - mas time,
B.
doo choo doo choo doo choo doo choo won - der - ful Christ - mas doo choo doo choo

29
S.
simply having a wonderful Christmas time.
A.
simply having a wonderful Christmas time.
T.
simply having a wonderful Christmas time.
B.
doo choo doo choo doo choo doo choo won-der-ful Christ-mas doo doo doo be doo
33
S.
doo doo wah wah wah wah wah wah doo doo wah wah wah wah wah wah
A.
doo doo wah wah wah wah wah wah doo doo wah wah wah wah wah wah
The par-ty's on, the feel-ing's here,
T.
doo doo wah wah wah wah wah wah doo doo wah wah wah wah wah wah
B.
The par-ty's on, the feel-ing's here,
doo tch tch tch ba doot doo tch tch tch ba doot

37
S.
doo doo wah wah wah wah wah wah doo doo wah wah wah wah wah wah
A.
doo doo wah wah wah wah wah wah doo doo wah wah wah wah wah wah
that on - ly comes this time of year.
T.
doo doo wah wah wah wah wah wah doo doo wah wah wah wah wah wah
B.
that on - ly comes this time of year.
doo tch tch tch ba doo doo tch tch ba doo doo doo doo

41
S.
Sim - ply hav - ing a won - der - ful Christ - mas time,
A.
Sim - ply hav - ing a won - der - ful Christ - mas time,
T.
Sim - ply hav - ing a won - der - ful Christ - mas time,
B.
doo choo doo choo doo choo doo choo won - der - ful Christ - mas doo choo doo choo

45
S.
sim - ply hav - ing a won - der - ful Christ-mas time.
A.
sim - ply hav - ing a won - der - ful Christ-mas time.
T.
sim - ply hav - ing a won - der - ful Christ-mas time.
B.
doo choo doo choo doo choo doo choo won - der - ful Christ-mas doo doot doo be doo

49
S.
legato
oo They've prac - tised
A.
marcato
legato
The choir of child - ren sing their song, they've prac - tised
T.
legato
oo They've prac - tised
B.
tch tch tch tch tch tch tch tch tch tch tch tch
marcato
legato
The choir of child - ren sing their song, they've prac - tised

55
cresc.
S.
all year long.
f
ding ding ding
dong dong
A.
ding ding ding ding ding ding ding ding ding
T.
all year long.
dong dong dong dong dong dong
B.
tch tch tch tch
ding dong ding dong ding dong ding dong ding dong ding dong
ding dong ding dong ding dong ding dong ding dong ding dong
60
ding
dong dong
ah
dim.
ding ding ding
oo
ah
oo
ah
dong dong
oo
dong dong dong dong
ding dong ding dong dong dong dong dong

65
mf
S.
Past three o' - clock on a
A.
Past three o' - clock on a
The word is out, a-bout the town.
T.
Past three o' - clock on a
B.
The word is out, a-bout the town.
ding dong ding dong ding dong ding dong ding dong ding dong ding dong ding dong
69
cold and frost - y morn - - ing.
cold and frost - y morn - - ing.
So raise a glass, oh, and don't look down.
cold and frost - y morn - - ing.
So raise a glass, oh, and don't look down.
ding dong ding dong ding dong ding dong ding dong ding dong ding dong ding dong

73
S.
Sim - ply hav - ing a won - der - ful Christ - mas time,
A.
Sim - ply hav - ing a won - der - ful Christ - mas time,
T.
Sim - ply hav - ing a won - der - ful Christ - mas time,
B.
doo choo doo choo doo choo doo choo won - der - ful Christ - mas doo choo doo choo

77
sim - ply hav - ing a won - der - ful Christ - mas time.
sim - ply hav - ing a won - der - ful Christ - mas time.
sim - ply hav - ing a won - der - ful Christ - mas time.
doo choo doo choo doo choo doo choo won - der - ful Christ - mas doo doo doo be doo

81
S.
legato
oo They've prac - tised
A.
marcato
The choir of child - ren sing their song, they've prac - tised
T.
legato
oo They've prac - tised
B.
tch tch tch tch tch tch tch tch tch tch tch tch
marcato
legato
The choir of child - ren sing their song, they've prac - tised

87
S.
cresc.
f
ding ding ding
all year long.
dong dong
A.
cresc.
f
all year long.
ding ding ding ding ding ding ding ding ding
T.
cresc.
f
all year long.
dong dong dong dong dong dong
B.
tch tch tch tch
f
ding dong ding dong ding dong ding dong ding dong ding dong
cresc.
f
all year long.
ding dong ding dong ding dong ding dong ding dong ding dong

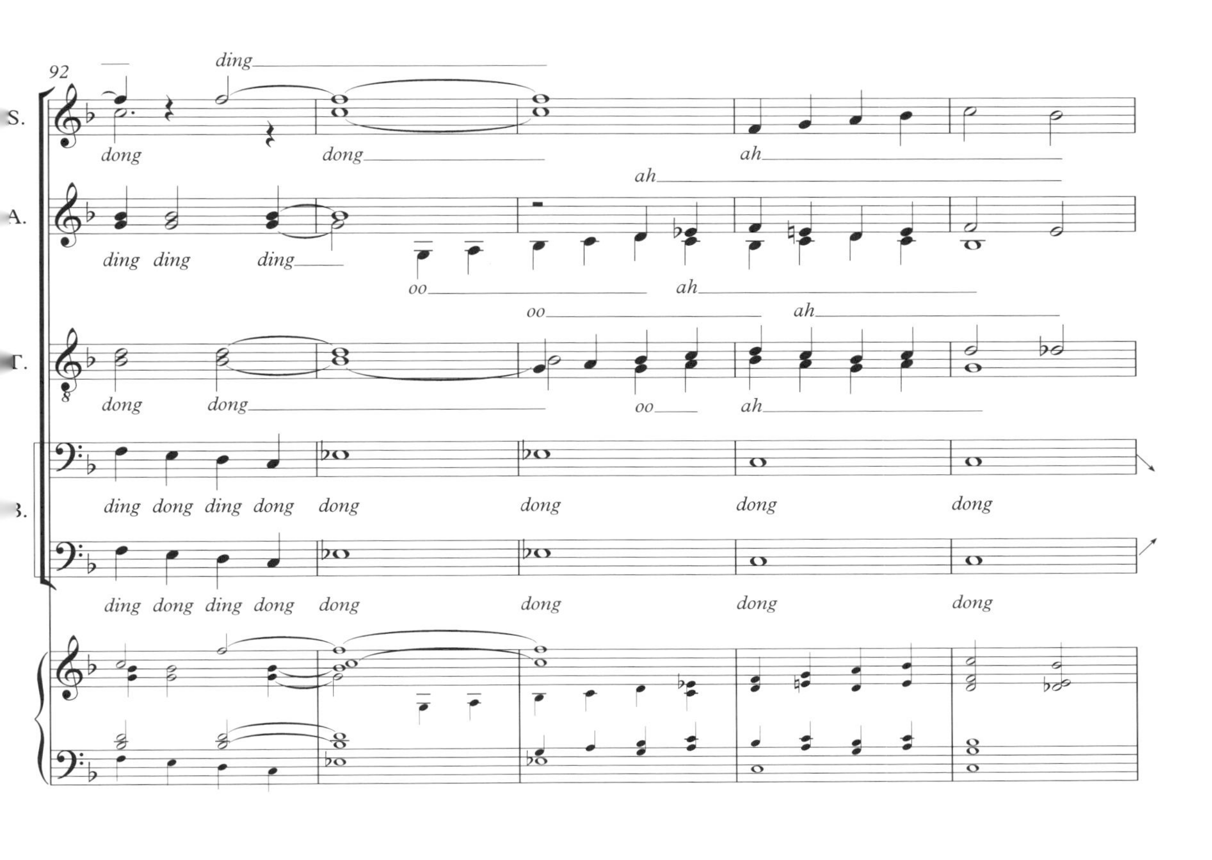
92
S.
ding
dong dong
ah
A.
ah
ding ding ding
oo ah
oo ah
T.
dong dong
oo ah
B.
ding dong ding dong dong dong dong dong
ding dong ding dong dong dong dong dong

97
ba dap ba ba ba dap ba ba
The party's on, the feel-ing's here,
ba dap ba ba ba dap ba ba
ba dap ba ba ba dap ba ba

101
S.
ba dap ba ba ba dap 'Cause we're
A.
that on - ly comes, oh, this time of year.
T.
ba dap ba ba ba dap 'Cause we're
B.
ba dap ba ba ba dap 'Cause we're

105
S.
sim - ply hav - ing a won - der - ful Christ - mas time.
A.
Sim - ply hav - ing a won - der - ful Christ - mas time.
T.
sim - ply hav - ing a won - der - ful Christ - mas time.
B.
doo choo doo choo doo choo doo choo won - der - ful Christ - mas doo choo doo choo

109
S.
Sim - ply hav - ing a won - der - ful, won - der - ful,
A.
Sim - ply hav - ing a won - der - ful, won - der - ful,
T.
Sim - ply hav - ing a won - der - ful, won - der - ful,
B.
doo choo doo choo doo choo doo choo won - der - ful, won - der - ful,
113
won - der - ful Christ - mas - time,
won - der - ful Christ - mas - time, Christ - mas
won - der - ful Christ - mas - time, won-der-ful time,
won - der - ful Christ - mas - time, Christ - mas
Christ - mas - time, Christ - mas
won - der - ful, Christ - mas ding dong ding dong ding dong ding dong

117
S.
Christ-mas - time,
won - der - ful
A.
time,
won - der - ful
time,
Christ - mas won - der - ful
T.
time,
Christ - mas, won - der - ful
time,
Christ - mas,
B.
ding dong ding dong ding dong ding dong won - der - ful
120
S.
Christ - mas - - time!
A.
Christ - mas - - time!
Christ - mas - - time!
T.
Christ - mas - - time!
B.
Christ - mas - - time!